JOURNAL

RECORD-KEEPING
FOR ALL UNIT STUDIES

TOPIC:

_____

COMPLETED BY:

_____

Journal:
Record-Keeping for All Unit Studies

ISBN 1-888306-02-5

Copyright © 1994 by Amanda Bennett

Published by:
Homeschool Press
229 S. Bridge St.
P.O. Box 254
Elkton, MD 21922-0254

Send requests for information to the above address.

Cover design by Mark Dinsmore.

This book is dedicated to

YOU!

Enjoy the adventure

of unit studies with your family!

Table of Contents

Introduction

This journal was developed in response to the growing number of requests for help with record-keeping for unit studies. It is my hope that the forms in the Journal will be a useful tool and easy for you to use, making your units more enjoyable. These forms were developed for use in our own family, and now that they are published, I myself am thrilled that they are now all bound in one place and easy for us to use.

This journal will enable you to record your resources, questions that the students have about the topic, field trips, assignments and even a daily log of your adventures in the study. In the back of the book, there are examples of how to use the different parts of the journal, along with blank pages for your own notes, photos and scrapbook pages. Please feel free to copy the pages for use with your own children.

Unit studies are such a wonderful learning adventure, and the paperwork should help build the unit, instead of dragging it down in drudgery. The arrangement of this journal should add to your studies and make it easier for you to see areas that you might have overlooked, as well as cutting down on all the loose scraps of paper and notes that are piling up. Take care and enjoy the adventure!

Amanda

OUR BOOK FRIENDS

These blank pages are for recording other bits and pieces of information and ideas that you want to remember about the study. Enjoy your unit study and the adventure!

What Do We Want to Investigate?

As you begin to work on a unit, take time to ask the students what they would like to know about the unit study topic. It helps to capture their interests on paper to make sure that their curiosity is answered during the course of the unit. This will give you an idea of areas that you might want to focus on more intensely.

Question 1:

(by_____)

_____

_____

_____ Where in the study will this be addressed?

_____

Question 2:

(by_____)

_____

_____

_____ Where in the study will this be addressed?

_____

Question 3:

(by_____)

_____

_____

_____ Where in the study will this be addressed?

_____

What Do We Want to Investigate?

Question 4:

(by _____)

_____

_____

_____ Where in the study will this be addressed?

_____

Question 5:

(by _____)

_____

_____

_____ Where in the study will this be addressed?

_____

Question 6:

(by _____)

_____

_____

_____Where in the study will this be addressed?

_____

What Do We Want to Investigate?

Question 8:

(by _____)

_____

_____

_____ Where in the study will this be addressed?

_____

Question 9:

(by _____)

_____

_____

_____ Where in the study will this be addressed?

_____

Question 10:

(by _____)

_____

_____

_____ Where in the study will this be addressed?

_____

Books That We Used

You will probably use many books during the process of working on a unit study—they are a valuable information source to use to learn more and explain more about the topic. The following pages are for keeping a record of these books. Our book notes and records have proven invaluable as we looked back to find a particular good book or author.

Research Topic Key Word: _____

Resource: Title: _____

             Author: _____

Publisher: _____

             Copyright Date: _____

             Topics Studied and Pages Used: _____

_____

_____

_____

_____

Research Topic Key Word: _____

Resource: Title: _____

             Author: _____

Publisher: _____

             Copyright Date: _____

             Topics Studied and Pages Used: _____

_____

_____

_____

_____

Books That We Used

*Research Topic Key Word:*_____

Resource: Title:_____

Author:_____

*Publisher:*_____

Copyright Date:_____

Topics Studied and Pages Used:_____

_____

_____

_____

_____

*Research Topic Key Word:*_____

Resource: Title:_____

Author:_____

*Publisher:*_____

Copyright Date:_____

Topics Studied and Pages Used:_____

_____

_____

_____

_____

Books That We Used

Research Topic Key Word: _____

Resource: Title: _____

  Author: _____

Publisher: _____

  Copyright Date: _____

  Topics Studied and Pages Used: _____

_____

_____

_____

_____

Research Topic Key Word: _____

Resource: Title: _____

  Author: _____

Publisher: _____

  Copyright Date: _____

  Topics Studied and Pages Used: _____

_____

_____

_____

_____

Books That We Used

Research Topic Key Word: _____

Resource: Title: _____

Author: _____

Publisher: _____

Copyright Date: _____

Topics Studied and Pages Used: _____

_____

_____

_____

_____

Research Topic Key Word: _____

Resource: Title: _____

Author: _____

Publisher: _____

Copyright Date: _____

Topics Studied and Pages Used: _____

_____

_____

_____

_____

Other Resources Used

In the process of working on a unit study, you will use other resources that will help explain more about the topic, as you progress. These might include music recordings, art selections, videos, games, professionals in a related area, museums, science centers, etc. The following pages are for keeping a record of these other resources that you used with this unit study.

Resource: _____

Details about the resource: (software, game, museum, etc.)

_____

_____

Things that were learned or observed using this resource:

_____

_____

_____

_____

Resource: _____

Details about the resource: (software, game, museum, etc.)

_____

_____

Things that were learned or observed using this resource:

_____

_____

_____

_____

OUR BOOK FRIENDS

Other Resources Used

Resource: _____

Details about the resource: (software, game, museum, etc.)

_____

_____

Things that were learned or observed using this resource:

_____

_____

_____

_____

Resource: _____

Details about the resource: (software, game, museum, etc.)

_____

_____

Things that were learned or observed using this resource:

_____

_____

_____

_____

Other Resources Used

Resource: _____

Details about the resource: (software, game, museum, etc.)

_____

_____

Things that were learned or observed using this resource:

_____

_____

_____

_____

Resource: _____

Details about the resource: (software, game, museum, etc.)

_____

_____

Things that were learned or observed using this resource:

_____

_____

_____

_____

Other Resources Used

Resource: _____

Details about the resource: (software, game, museum, etc.)

_____

_____

Things that were learned or observed using this resource:

_____

_____

_____

_____

Resource: _____

Details about the resource: (software, game, museum, etc.)

_____

_____

Things that were learned or observed using this resource:

_____

_____

_____

_____

Our Activities and Projects

As you work on a unit study with your family, try to include some hands-on activities that will introduce some of the concepts of the unit. These pages have been included for you to record the details of these activities and projects, which might include building models, making costumes, making videos, developing collections, etc.

Activity or Project: _____

Educational Focus: _____

Details and Notes: _____

_____

_____

_____

_____

_____

_____

_____

Sketches or Photos:

Our Activities and Projects

Activity or Project: _____

Educational Focus: _____

Details and Notes: _____

_____

_____

_____

_____

_____

_____

_____

Sketches or Photos:

Our Activities and Projects

Activity or Project: _____

Educational Focus: _____

Details and Notes: _____

_____

_____

_____

_____

_____

_____

Sketches or Photos:

Our Activities and Projects

Activity or Project: _____

Educational Focus: _____

Details and Notes: _____

_____

_____

_____

_____

_____

_____

_____

Sketches or Photos:

Adventure Log

Use this log sheet to record the daily activities of each child, noting the pages that have been read, tasks that have been accomplished and progress that has been made. Use the column down the left to record the dates and the columns across the right for each student.

Students' Names

Date					

OUR BOOK FRIENDS

Adventure Log

Use this log sheet to record the daily activities of each child, noting the pages that have been read, tasks that have been accomplished and progress that has been made. Use the column down the left to record the dates and the columns across the right for each student.

Students' Names

Date					

Adventure Log

Use this log sheet to record the daily activities of each child, noting the pages that have been read, tasks that have been accomplished and progress that has been made. Use the column down the left to record the dates and the columns across the right for each student.

Students' Names

Date					

Adventure Log

Use this log sheet to record the daily activities of each child, noting the pages that have been read, tasks that have been accomplished and progress that has been made. Use the column down the left to record the dates and the columns across the right for each student.

Students' Names

Date					

Adventure Log

Use this log sheet to record the daily activities of each child, noting the pages that have been read, tasks that have been accomplished and progress that has been made. Use the column down the left to record the dates and the columns across the right for each student.

Students' Names

Date					

Adventure Log

Use this log sheet to record the daily activities of each child, noting the pages that have been read, tasks that have been accomplished and progress that has been made. Use the column down the left to record the dates and the columns across the right for each student.

Students' Names

Date					

Independent Reading

As you progress through a unit study, encourage independent reading for those that are old enough to read, and read aloud or along with those not quite reading on their own yet. The Independent Reading pages that follow have been included for you to record the books that the children read during this unit.

Book Title	Author	Child	Comments

Independent Reading

Book Title	Author	Child	Comments

Independent Reading

Book Title	Author	Child	Comments

OUR BOOK FRIENDS

Independent Reading

Book Title	Author	Child	Comments

Our Family Reading

When working on a unit, read aloud together as a family and discuss what was read. This process helps us each share comments and learn to hear other people's ideas. It also provides some wonderful family time. These pages have been included for recording the books that you read together, along with your comments and perhaps some favorite quotes from the books.

Book Title: _____

    Author: _____

    Publisher: _____

    Comments: _____

_____

_____

_____

_____

_____

Book Title: _____

    Author: _____

    Publisher: _____

    Comments: _____

_____

_____

_____

_____

_____

Our Family Reading

Book Title: _____

    Author: _____

    Publisher: _____

    Comments: _____

_____

_____

_____

_____

_____

Book Title: _____

    Author: _____

    Publisher: _____

    Comments: _____

_____

_____

_____

_____

Our Field Trips

As you work on a unit study, develop some meaningful field trips that will add to the learning experience of the unit. The following Field Trip pages have been included for you to record the details of these trips. Please do not forget to send a thank you note to the places that you visit!

Field Trip To: _____

Location: _____

_____

Telephone Number: _____

Contact Person: _____

Date of the Trip: _____

Details of the Trip: _____

_____

_____

_____

_____

_____

_____

Sketches or Photos:

Our Field Trips

Field Trip To: _____

Location: _____

Telephone Number: _____

Contact Person: _____

Date of the Trip: _____

Details of the Trip: _____

_____

_____

_____

_____

_____

_____

Sketches or Photos:

Our Field Trips

Field Trip To: _____

Location: _____

Telephone Number: _____

Contact Person: _____

Date of the Trip: _____

Details of the Trip: _____

_____

_____

_____

_____

_____

_____

Sketches or Photos:

Our Field Trips

Field Trip To: _____

Location: _____

Telephone Number: _____

Contact Person: _____

Date of the Trip: _____

Details of the Trip: _____

_____

_____

_____

_____

_____

_____

Sketches or Photos:

Our Field Trips

Field Trip To: _____

Location: _____

Telephone Number: _____

Contact Person: _____

Date of the Trip: _____

Details of the Trip: _____

_____

_____

_____

_____

_____

_____

Sketches or Photos:

OUR BOOK FRIENDS

Assignments

The next few pages have been included for the purpose of recording special assignments, such as research assignments, writing assignments and other special tasks for the students.

Task: _____

_____

Assigned To: _____

Date Assigned: _____

Completed: _____

Task: _____

_____

Assigned To: _____

Date Assigned: _____

Completed: _____

Task: _____

_____

Assigned To: _____

Date Assigned: _____

Completed: _____

Task: _____

_____

Assigned To: _____

Date Assigned: _____

Completed: _____

Assignments

Task: _____

_____

Assigned To: _____

Date Assigned: _____

Completed: _____

Task: _____

_____

Assigned To: _____

Date Assigned: _____

Completed: _____

Task: _____

_____

Assigned To: _____

Date Assigned: _____

Completed: _____

Task: _____

_____

Assigned To: _____

Date Assigned: _____

Completed: _____

Assignments

Task: _____

_____

Assigned To: _____

Date Assigned: _____

Completed: _____

Task: _____

_____

Assigned To: _____

Date Assigned: _____

Completed: _____

Task: _____

_____

Assigned To: _____

Date Assigned: _____

Completed: _____

Task: _____

_____

Assigned To: _____

Date Assigned: _____

Completed: _____

Examples

On these Example pages, I have used a unit study on Oceans to demonstrate how you can use the individual forms.

What Do We Want To Investigate?

Question 1:

(by ___Susan___)

How do whales talk?

Where in the study will this be addressed?

In the section on Ocean Mammals

Books That We Used

Research Topic Key Word: Ocean Currents

Resource: Title: The Ocean Book

Author: The Center for Marine Conservation

Publisher: John Wiley & Sons, Inc., New York

Copyright Date: 1989

Topics Studied and Pages Used:

Page 17: Description of currents

Pages 18-19: Experiments with different kinds of currents

Other Resources Used

Resource: Krill: A Whale of a Game

Details about the resource: (software, game, museum, etc.)

Card game that the older children played, from Ampersand Press

Things that were learned or observed using this resource:

It taught about the ocean food chain and ocean life

Examples

Our Activities and Projects

Activity or Project: Shell Collection

Educational Focus: Sea Life and Mollusks

Details and Notes: The children collected shells on a regular basis from the local beach and from the Gulf Coast. They classified and labelled each shell.

Our Field Trips

Field Trip To: Brevard Science Center

Location: Eau Gallie, Florida

Date of the Trip: January 14, 1994

Details of the Trip: We went to the Science Center to see their special display on Sharks, and participate in a hands-on class on shark dissection. It was a thorough display and the children talked about everything there for some time afterwards, drawing sketches and reading the shark books from the library with new interest.

Assignments

Task: Build a model of a tidal basin that is like the one at Sebastian Inlet, using plaster of Paris and anything else in the project cabinet.

Assigned To: Johnny

Date Assigned: January 10, 1994

Completed: January 24, 1994

Our Notes and Ideas

Our Notes and Ideas

Our Notes and Ideas

About The Author

Amanda Bennett, author and speaker, wife and mother of three, holds a degree in mechanical engineering. She has written this ever-growing series of unit studies for her own children, to capture their enthusiasm and nurture their gifts and talents. The concept of a thematic approach to learning is a simple one. Amanda will share this simplification through her books, allowing others to use these unit study guides to discover the amazing world that God has created for us all.

Science can be a very intimidating subject to teach, and Amanda has written this series to include science with other important areas of curriculum that apply naturally to each topic. The guides allow more time to be spent enjoying the unit study, instead of spending weeks of research time to prepare for each unit. She has shared the results of her research in the guides, including plenty of resources for areas of the study, spelling and vocabulary lists, fiction and nonfiction titles, possible careers within the topic, writing ideas, activity suggestions, addresses of manufacturers, teams, and other helpful resources.

The science-based series of guides currently includes the Unit Study Adventures titles:

Baseball	Homes
Computers	Oceans
Elections	Olympics
Electricity	Pioneers
Flight	Space
Gardens	Trains

The holiday-based series of guides currently includes the Unit Study Adventures titles:

Christmas
Thanksgiving

This planned 40-book series will soon include additional titles, which will be released periodically. We appreciate your interest. "Enjoy the Adventure."